I N S I G H T S T U D I E S

WHERE TO LORD?

6 STUDIES ON GUIDANCE FOR SMALL GROUPS AND INDIVIDUALS

BY TONY PAYNE AND SIMON ROBERTS

CONTENTS

Introduction to the studies 5

STUDY 1: Where to, Lord? 9

STUDY 2: Responding to God 15

STUDY 3: Hear the word of the Lord! 21

STUDY 4: The experience of guidance 29

STUDY 5: The beginning of wisdom 37

STUDY 6: Case study—work 45

APPENDIX 1: Course overview 51

APPENDIX 2: Suggested timing for each study 55

INTRODUCTION TO THE STUDIES

How to make the most of these studies

While your Bible might come complete with a topical index, this certainly wasn't part of the original. In fact the Bible was written by many different human authors over many hundreds of years. Yet because God is the ultimate author, the Bible makes sense as a whole and has much to say about a vast range of topics. This Bible study is designed to help you examine one of these topics: guidance.

Perhaps the best way to study this topic would be to read the Bible cover to cover and make your own topical index! Having discovered all the parts of the Bible which talk about this topic you could then put all the pieces of the jigsaw together and summarize what the Bible as a whole says about guidance. However, most of us would benefit from a bit more guidance on guidance, and this is where this Bible study and the accompanying DVD can help.

This workbook will give you the road map for each study, including Bible passages to investigate and questions to think through. At various points you will be prompted to play a section of the accompanying DVD, where the Bible's teaching on guidance will be summarized and explained. Between your own investigation and discussion, and the teaching material presented on the DVD, we trust you will gain greater insight into this topic—seeing for yourself what the Bible has to say.

The format

Each study has up to four different types of material, each having its own symbol.

 For starters: Questions to break the ice and get you thinking.

 Investigate: Questions to help you investigate key parts of the Bible.

 Look and listen: Video segments which summarize the Bible's teaching on a particular topic, integrating the Bible passages you have read and prompting you to think through the implications for yourself. It is a good idea to make notes during the video in the spaces provided in this workbook.

 Think it through: Questions to help you think through the implications of your discoveries and write down your own thoughts and reactions.

Suggestions for individual study

Before you begin, pray that God would open your eyes to what he is saying in his word and give you the spiritual strength to do something about it. You may be spurred to pray again at the end of the study.

Work through the study, following the directions as you go. Write in the spaces provided.

Resist the temptation to skip over the **Think it through** sections. It is important to think about what is said in the video presentations (rather than just accepting them as true) and to ponder the implications for your life. Writing these things down is a very valuable way to get your thoughts working.

Take what opportunities you can to talk to others about what you've learnt.

Suggestions for group study

Much of the above applies to group study as well. The studies are suitable for structured Bible study or home groups, as well as for more informal pairs and threesomes. Each study is designed to take just under an hour to complete, although you may want to allow extra time if you want to discuss the material in more detail.

Everyone will get more out of the studies if each member of the group has done some preparation *beforehand*. In particular, people should work through the **For starters** and **Investigate** sections, making notes in the space provided. If people have worked through these sections then there should be plenty of time to watch the video material and discuss the **Think it through** questions.

Spend most of the group time discussing the **Investigate** *and* **Think it through** *sections*. If people have done some homework then you should be able to focus on what the passages mean, rather than on finding and reading them.

The role of the group leader is to direct the course of the discussion and to try to draw the threads together at the end. This will mean a little extra preparation—watching all the video sections for each study, working out which questions are worth concentrating on, and being sure of the main thrust of the study. To help group leaders understand the logic of the course and of each study, Appendix 1 on page 51 contains a course overview. Leaders will also probably want to work out approximately how long they want to spend on each part. See Appendix 2 for suggested timings for each study.

Check before the study commences that the DVD is properly loaded and cued to the right starting point. Make sure that everyone can see and hear the video presentations.

We haven't included an 'answers guide' to the questions in the studies. This is deliberate, for we want to give you a guided tour, not a lecture. However, there is more than enough information on the accompanying DVD to set you on the right path. The rest is up to you.

If you would like to do some further investigation into guidance, we highly recommend reading *Guidance and the Voice of God* (see p. 57 for more details). It is also the ideal way for group leaders to do some extra preparation, since it provides further information and additional examples and case studies.

WHERE TO, LORD?

For starters
We all have to make choices and decisions

1. What decisions did you make today?

2. What big decisions do you think you will make in the next 5-10 years?

3. How do you feel when having to make these big decisions?

Look and listen
Study 1: INTRODUCTION

Investigate

1. Read 1 Chronicles 29:10-13.
   What is God's basic relationship to the created world?

2. Skim through the following verses. How far does God's power and control extend over the world? What is he able to do?

   Jeremiah 32:17, 26-27

Proverbs 21:1

Matthew 10:29

Acts 2:23

3. Look quickly at the following verses. What do they tell us about what God is like, and what he does for his people?

Nehemiah 9:6-15

Psalms 78:51-55

Ezekiel 34:11-16

John 10:24-28

Look and listen

Study 1: GOD THE GUIDE

Investigate

1. Read Ephesians 1:3-10.
   a. What does this passage tell us about God's will, his grand plan and purpose for all things (i.e. vv. 9-10)?

   b. Verse 4 tells us that we have been chosen to be _____ and _____.

   c. Verse 5 tell us that we have been predestined _____ _____ through Jesus Christ.

2. Read 1 Peter 1:3-5. For what purpose has God caused us to be born again? What are the characteristics of the final goal he has in store for us?

3. Ephesians 2:8-10 tells us that we are God's workmanship. Why has God 'created' us again in Christ Jesus?

4. Read 1 Thessalonians 4:1-8. What is God's will for us in this passage? What various aspects are mentioned?

Look and listen
Study 1: ALL UNDER CHRIST

Think it through

1. What is the biggest decision we face in life? What guidance does God offer for this decision?

2. We are all tempted to make decisions based on our own desires; we tend only to think about God's goal for our lives afterwards. How is this tendency reflected in your life?

3. If you know that Jesus is the ruler of all things, how should this change the way you make decisions?

RESPONDING TO GOD

Last study we saw the grand plan God has for his world, a plan having Christ at the very centre. We saw that God is guiding all things under the rule of his son, Jesus. Let's recap by watching the introduction video for this study.

Look and listen
Study 2: INTRODUCTION

Investigate

1. Read the following verses and write down what they tell us about how we should respond to the gospel. (You might like to divide up these passages among your group.)

   Mark 1:15, 8:34

John 6:28-29

Acts 20:21

2 Corinthians 5:15

1 Thessalonians 1:9-10

1 John 3:23, 5:1-2

 Look and listen
Study 2: RIGHT RESPONSES

Think it through

1. What is the difference between repentance and 'feeling sorry'?

2. If repentance is not something that happens only once in the Christian life, what does it mean to repent in an ongoing way?

3. What would you say to a person who said, "I wish I had your faith"?

4. "Faith is believing something to be true apart from proof." What is wrong with this common definition of faith?

5. What is the relationship between faith and obedience?

6. Why are faith and repentance so central to God's guidance of us? How can we make sure they remain central to our lives?

Look and listen

Study 2: WRONG RESPONSES

Think it through

1. Look at Titus' actions in 2 Corinthians 8:16-17.
   a. How many different 'causes' can you find for what Titus did?

   b. What does this tell us about the way God's sovereign power works in our lives?

2. What is wrong with the view that we can choose 'God's second best', and somehow fall outside of his plan?

3. Are you sometimes tempted to be envious of those who reject God's ways and seem to profit from doing so? Read Psalm 37:1-9. What warnings and encouragement does the Bible offer us when we are tempted to reject God's goodness?

HEAR THE WORD OF THE LORD!

So far we have seen that God is guiding all things under the rule of his son, Jesus. Repentance and faith in Christ are therefore at the very centre of God's message to us. Let's recap by watching the introduction video for this study.

Look and listen
Study 3: INTRODUCTION

Investigate

Read Hebrews 1:1-4.

1. How has God spoken in the past?

2. From the following passages, list the different ways in which God has revealed himself to people. (You might like to divide up these passages among your group.)

   Exodus 3:1-6

   Exodus 20:22

   Numbers 22:28-33

   1 Kings 14:17-18

   1 Samuel 3:1-9

   Isaiah 1:1, 2:1

   Ezekiel 1:1-3

Daniel 5:1-6,23-24

Exodus 24:4

Jeremiah 30:2

Isaiah 30:8

3. How has God spoken to us in these last days (Heb 1:1-2)?

4. What docs Hebrews 1:1-3 tell us about the Son?

5. Read John 12:49 and John 14:6-10. What does Jesus say about himself and his words in these passages?

Look and listen
Study 3: GOD'S SPOKESMAN

Investigate

1. Read Matthew 28:16-20.
   a. What does Jesus claim about himself?

   b. What responsibility does Jesus give to his apostles?

2. Read 1 John 1:1-3. What is it that John makes known to his readers? What is the basis for the confidence he has in his message?

3. Read 2 Timothy 3:14-17.
   a. Scripture is able to make us wise for _____.

   b. For what things is the word of God useful and profitable?

   c. For what does the word of God equip us?

4. Read 2 Corinthians 11:13-15 and 1 John 4:1-6.
   a. What threat do these passages warn us of?

   b. What tests does John give in order to discern the truth?

Think it through

1. Does God speak to us today through the Scriptures? In what ways has this been your experience?

2. If someone comes to us and says, "I have a word from God", how do we know if it really is from God or not?

Look and listen

Study 3: GOD'S WORD IN SCRIPTURE

Think it through

1. Do you sometimes think God is distant and silent? Where should we turn at those times?

2. If the Bible is the only place we find God's authoritative word to us, what implications does this have for discovering God's will?

3. What problems arise when we do not give the Bible's message the supreme and central place it deserves as God's word to us?

THE EXPERIENCE OF GUIDANCE

God is guiding all things under the rule of his son, Jesus. Therefore, repentance and faith in Christ are at the very centre of God's message to us, a message that we come to know through his living word, the Bible. Let's begin by watching the introduction video for this study.

Look and listen

Study 4: INTRODUCTION

Investigate

1. Read Job 1:6-19.
   a. What was the real reason for the dreadful things that happened? Did Job know this?

   b. How did Job's wife interpret the circumstances (Job 2:9)?

   c. Also read Job 8:1-6. How does Bildad interpret what has happened to Job and his children?

2. Read Isaiah 10:5-7.
   a. Why did God send Assyria to attack Israel?

   b. What did the Assyrians themselves think they were doing?

c. Simply by observing what happened, how could the Israelites tell whether they were being punished, or whether their situation was like Job's?

3. Read John 9:1-3. How did the disciples read the circumstances of the man's blindness? Were they right?

4. Read Deuteronomy 13:1-5, 18:20-22. What two tests were Israel to use in determining whether a prophet or dreamer was really speaking the word of the Lord?

   (You might also like to look up 1 John 4:1-6, or check question 4b on page 26 of your workbook to remind yourself of the tests that the apostle John gives.)

Look and listen

Study 4: LOOKING THROUGH BIBLE GLASSES

Think it through

1. Think back over the example of Job.
   a. Was God completely and sovereignly in control of what happened to Job? (Look at Job's final response in 42:1-3.)

b. Did Job know in advance what God's purpose was?

c. Did God achieve his purpose anyway?

2. What problems are associated with trying to 'read' God's will for our lives from our circumstances or feelings?

3. John Calvin describes Scripture as being like a pair of glasses which 'clearly shows us the true God'. How does this help us understand the proper relationship between the Bible and our experiences/feelings?

> *Just as old or bleary-eyed men and those with weak vision, if you thrust before them a most beautiful volume, even if they recognize it to be some sort of writing, yet can scarcely construe two words, but with the aid of spectacles will begin to read distinctly; so Scripture, gathering up the otherwise confused knowledge of God in our minds, having dispersed our dullness, clearly shows us the true God. (Institutes I.VI.1)*

Look and listen

Study 4: TWO FORMS OF GUIDANCE

Think it through

1. Complete the following table by circling your answers in each column, then discuss.

	Behind-the-Scenes Guidance (God's sovereign control of all that happens in our lives)	Conscious Co-operation Guidance (God's direction of us through his word)
In this type of guidance we know what God is up to in advance.	True / False	True / False
In this type of guidance what God is doing remains hidden from us and beyond our understanding.	True / False	True / False
God uses this type of guidance for the good of those who love him.	True / False	True / False
This type of guidance is clear and unambiguous to us.	True / False	True / False
This type of guidance is given to us so that we might make decisions, i.e. be obedient to it.	True / False	True / False
Knowing about this type of guidance should lead us to trust God and praise him for his dependability.	True / False	True / False

2. Some Christians have experiences which they understand to be God guiding them in a particular direction (that is, in a 'conscious cooperation' sense). What are we to make of these?

3. If God is always guiding us 'behind the scenes', how should we talk about our daily experiences and the things that happen to us, both good and bad?

THE BEGINNING OF WISDOM

God is guiding all things under the rule of his son, Jesus. Therefore, repentance and faith in Christ are at the very centre of God's message to us, a message that we come to know through his word, the Bible. This living word of God makes sense of the world and our experiences, and is the sure ground upon which we can base our decisions. Let's recap by watching the introduction video for this study.

Look and listen

Study 5: INTRODUCTION

Investigate

1. Read Proverbs 9, and fill in the table.

	Wisdom	Folly
General characteristics		
Who is it for?		
What results?		

2. Read Proverbs 15:17 and 24:27
   a. Summarize the wisdom of each verse in your own words.

b. Do these verses tell us anything that a person couldn't have figured out for themselves just by using 'common sense'?

3. Read Colossians 2:1-10.
   a. Where is ultimate wisdom found?

   b. Why is it important for Christians to understand this wisdom?

 Think it through

1. Is it possible for the same action to be perfectly acceptable in one context but wrong in another? Why/why not?

2. What is the difference, if any, between calling something 'foolish' and calling it 'wrong'?

Look and listen
Study 5: WISDOM

Think it through

1. What do you think marks someone out as a wise person? How can a person grow in wisdom?

2. How can we know if something is a matter of good judgement, or righteousness, or triviality? On what basis should we decide?

3. If the Bible seems silent on an issue, such as stem cell research or euthanasia, does this mean that it must not be a matter of righteousness? Why?

4. Do you think going to church is a matter of righteousness, good judgement or triviality? Why?

(If you want to spend some time on this question you might like to look at the following passages: Hebrews 10:24-25, Ephesians 1:22, Ephesians 5:23-32, Acts 20:28, 1 Tim 3:15.)

Look and listen
Study 5: TO SUM UP

Think it through

How has your thinking on guidance been challenged over the course of these studies? How do you need to change as a result?

CASE STUDY: WORK

This study gives you the chance to think through how what we have learnt about guidance applies to a particular topic—work.

Let's begin by watching the introduction video for this study.

Look and listen

Study 6: INTRODUCTION

Investigate

1. Work in creation

Read Genesis 1:26-28, 2:15.

What do these verses tell us about:

a. God and work?

b. the work God gave to humanity?

c. the value of work?

2. Work in a fallen world

Read Genesis 3:17-19; Ecclesiastes 2:4-11; Romans 8:20-22.

a. What should we expect work to be normally like, this side of the fall?

b. Is 'job satisfaction' something we should expect from our work? What should be our reaction if we do enjoy our jobs?

3. Why do we work?

Read Proverbs 28:19, 21:25-26; Ephesians 4:28; 2 Thessalonians 3:6-14.

a. In these passages, what reasons are given for working?

b. Why is work an act of love?

4. How to work

Read Exodus 20:8-11; Leviticus 19:13; Luke 3:12-14; Colossians 3:22-4:1.

Jot down everything you learn from these passages about *how* we are to work. What behaviour does God expect of his people in their work?

Look and listen

Study 6: WORK

Think it through

1. Given what we've learnt in this study, what 'work' decisions would be put under:
   a. matters of righteousness?

b. matters of good judgement?

c. matters of triviality?

2. Work in our modern world is very often about career, fulfilment, status and power. Discuss how God's view of work impacts on:
   a. the status we give to some jobs and not others;

   b. the idea that we should find our meaning and fulfilment through our work;

   c. the importance of 'job satisfaction'.

Look and listen
Study 6: TO SUM UP

You might like to spend some time praying about the things you have learnt during the course of these studies.

APPENDIX 1

COURSE OVERVIEW

Where to, Lord? is a series of six studies on the topic of guidance. The 'Introduction to the studies' on page 5 of this workbook tells you more about the studies and how to use them. This overview section is designed to explain briefly the logical connections between the six studies so that the study leader has a better understanding of the flow of the course.

Study 1: Where to, Lord?

Study 1 aims to teach people that God has a plan for his world. It is meaningless to talk about guidance if God hasn't got a plan. Because God made and owns everything, he is in control of everything. Furthermore, the Bible says very clearly that God is more than capable of making sure his plan is brought to fulfilment.

The main point of this study is that God's plan focuses on Christ Jesus. God's plan is for all people to be brought under the lordship of Christ; for those adopted as his sons and daughters to walk in holiness and righteousness; and for his children to eventually inherit his everlasting kingdom. This is God's plan. He does not have two plans: one general and one special. His one plan is both general and special. He wants all people—corporately and individually—to submit to Christ, and his plan for each Christian is to make them like Christ.

Study 2: Responding to God

Study 2 examines how we should respond to God and his plan. Our part in God guiding us has much less to do with discerning the will of God, and much more to do with trusting that God's plan is a good one, than we might commonly think. The right way to respond is through faith and repentance. This study examines what these are and what these are not.

Repentance is about turning our lives around and living life with Jesus as our Lord. The vast majority of the time it's clear what submitting to Jesus means, so the real task for us is to get on with the job.

There are, of course, wrong ways in which we can respond to God's revealed plan. We can reject what God tells us because we don't trust God, or because we think we will miss out on some good thing. But we can also reject God's guidance because we think God is not able to bring his good plan into effect. The idea that we can miss out on 'Plan A' in God's design, and therefore have to settle for 'Plan B' or 'Plan C' (i.e. God's second-best), is false. We cannot fall outside of God's plans for our lives, and we cannot, by our lack of trust or obedience, somehow short-circuit God's plan so that he cannot bring about his purposes. Despite our failings, God is able to transform us into Christlikeness.

Study 3: Hear the word of the Lord!

Where do we hear the word of God so that we might trust and obey it? Study 3 examines the answer to this question. As Hebrews 1 tells us, in the past God spoke in many ways at various times, but now he has spoken fully and finally by his Son, Jesus. It is to Jesus that we should turn to hear the word of God, for he is the one who reveals the Father, speaks the truth, and—in dying and rising to life—brings to fulfilment God's plan to reconcile humanity to himself.

Furthermore, Jesus gave authority to the apostles to speak this word of God to the world. The record of this message—the New Testament— is a great blessing for us who live 2,000 years after Jesus walked the face of the earth. Jesus speaks to us today through the Scriptures as the Spirit of God applies them to our hearts and minds.

As we read the Bible, we hear God speak. The Bible is not just one of many ways in which God guides; it is the *only* way by which God has *promised* to reveal his will. The Bible is the only place we can hear a sure and certain word from God. We should not expect God to reveal his will other than by the Scriptures because, firstly, God has not promised to guide us in any other way, and, secondly, it would be rather strange for God to speak in new and different ways, given Jesus' place as the full and final revelation of God.

Study 4: The experience of guidance

The problem most people are left with at this point is experience. Almost everyone accepts that God guides through Scripture. But many people don't accept that the Scriptures are the only sure and certain way to hear God speak. What about circumstances, strong feelings, inner promptings and other alleged 'words' from God? This study gives people the chance to think through the place of our experience in God's guidance.

Ultimately our experience and circumstances are ambiguous, and they can only be properly understood when viewed through 'Bible glasses'. The Bible explains our experience, and our experience should never usurp the Bible as the source of our knowledge of God. The Bible tells us that God is at work in everything 'behind-the-scenes', bringing his plan for us and the world to fulfilment. God's 'behind-the-scenes' guidance is always for our good, but it is not a clear word we should obey. Rather, the Bible alone is the clear word we have been given so that we might consciously cooperate with the guidance it gives: trusting God, speaking the truth, loving our enemies, being kind and generous, etc.

Study 5: The beginning of wisdom

There are, of course, many decisions about which the Bible appears to say nothing. Who should I marry? What job should I take? Where should I send my kids to school?

The first thing the Bible does tell us is which matters matter. Often the decisions we think are big turn out to be much less important. The question of which car to buy is much less important than how you are going to drive it. The Bible helps us to know which things are matters of righteousness, which things are matters of good judgement, and which things are trivialities.

If a decision is a matter of righteousness, the decision is easy: do what is right. Trivialities are neither here nor there, so these decisions should be made quickly and with minimal effort. Matters of good judgement are the ones that usually cause us problems. We know we should marry a Christian—preferably a Christian who is committed to godliness—but how do we choose which godly Christian to marry? There is no right and wrong answer to a question like this, for there is no one person who fits the Bible's criteria. Instead, there are many, and if you're fortunate enough to be able to choose between two (or more!) godly people, then you can't make a wrong decision. However, wisdom can help you make decisions with better consequences. This study examines the issue of wisdom.

Study 6: Case study—work

The final study gives people a chance to apply the previous five weeks of teaching to the topic of work.

SUGGESTED TIMING FOR EACH STUDY

Not all questions are created equal! Particularly with a topical study such as this one, some questions are designed to help you note a simple point that a passage makes, while other questions will take longer to talk over properly.

Remember, the aim of these studies is to gain a better understanding of guidance, and not to look at every passage in such fine detail that every last ounce of meaning is extracted. Each passage *should* be taken in context and correctly understood, but the focus is on putting all the pieces of the guidance 'jigsaw' together. So you should leave plenty of time for discussion. It won't help the group if you spend all your time on the **Investigate** sections without leaving enough time for the **Think it through** sections.

To help group leaders estimate how long to spend on each section of the studies, we have included the following 'run-sheets'. These assume that each study takes one hour, so if your group meets for longer you will need to modify the timings accordingly. To do the study in an hour, each member should have already looked up each passage and made notes in their workbook. You should also make sure you have the DVD loaded and ready to start at the introduction section for that study.

Study 1: Where to, Lord?

Section	Suggested Timing	Your Timing
For starters	7 min	
Look and listen: Introduction	3 min	3 min
Investigate	15 min	
Look and listen: God the guide	2 min	2 min
Investigate	15 min	
Look and listen: All under Christ	2 min	2 min
Think it through	15 min	
TOTAL	59 min	

Study 2: Responding to God

Section	Suggested Timing	Your Timing
Look and listen: Introduction	1 min	1 min
Investigate	10 min	
Look and listen: Right responses	6 min	6 min
Think it through	20 min	
Look and listen: Wrong responses	5 min	5 min
Think it through	18 min	
TOTAL	60 min	

Study 3: Hear the word of the Lord!

Section	Suggested Timing	Your Timing
Look and listen: Introduction	2 min	2 min
Investigate	10 min	
Look and listen: God's spokesman	3 min	3 min
Investigate	10 min	
Think it through	15 min	
Look and listen: God's word in Scripture	5 min	5 min
Think it through	15 min	
TOTAL	60 min	

Study 4: The experience of guidance

Section	Suggested Timing	Your Timing
Look and listen: Introduction	2 min	2 min
Investigate	10 min	
Look and listen: Looking through Bible glasses	7 min	7 min
Think it through	15 min	
Look and listen: Two forms of guidance	5 min	5 min
Think it through	20 min	
TOTAL	59 min	

Study 5: The beginning of wisdom

Section	Suggested Timing	Your Timing
Look and listen: Introduction	4 min	4 min
Investigate	7 min	
Think it through	10 min	
Look and listen: Wisdom	7 min	7 min
Think it through	20 min	
Look and listen: To sum up	2 min	2 min
Think it through	10 min	
TOTAL	60 min	

Study 6: Case study—work

Section	Suggested Timing	Your Timing
Look and listen: Introduction	1 min	1 min
Investigate	20 min	
Look and listen: Work	4 min	4 min
Think it through	30 min	
Look and listen: To sum up	2 min	2 min
TOTAL	57 min	

Matthias Media is a ministry team of like-minded, evangelical Christians working together to achieve a particular goal, as summarized in our mission statement:

To serve our Lord Jesus Christ, and the growth of his gospel in the world, by producing and delivering high quality, Bible-based resources.

It was in 1988 that we first started pursuing this mission together, and in God's kindness we now have more than 250 different ministry resources being distributed all over the world. These resources range from Bible studies and books, through to training courses and audio sermons.

To find out more about our large range of very useful products, and to access samples and free downloads, visit our website:

www.matthiasmedia.com.au

How to purchase our resources

1. Through a range of outlets in various parts of the world: visit **www.matthiasmedia.com.au/contact/overseas.htm** for details about recommended retailers in your part of the world.

2. Direct from us over the internet:
   – in the US: www.matthiasmedia.com
   – in Australia and the rest of the world: www.matthiasmedia.com.au

3. Direct from us by phone:
   – within Australia: 1800 814 360 (Sydney: 9663 1478)
   – international: +61-2-9663-1478

4. Trade enquiries worldwide:
   – email us: sales@matthiasmedia.com.au

Other Interactive and Topical Bible Studies from Matthias Media:

Our Interactive Bible Studies (IBS) and Topical Bible Studies (TBS) are another valuable resource to help you keep feeding from God's Word. The IBS series works through passages and books of the Bible; the TBS series pulls together the Bible's teaching on topics, such as money or prayer. As at November 2006, the series contains the following titles:

Beyond Eden
(GENESIS 1-11)
Authors: Phillip Jensen and Tony Payne, 9 studies

Out of Darkness
(EXODUS 1-18)
Author: Andrew Reid, 8 studies

The One and Only
(DEUTERONOMY)
Author: Bryson Smith, 8 studies

The Good, the Bad & the Ugly
(JUDGES)
Author: Mark Baddeley, 10 studies

Famine & Fortune
(RUTH)
Authors: Barry Webb and David Höhne, 4 studies

Renovator's Dream
(NEHEMIAH)
Authors: Phil Campbell and Greg Clarke, 7 studies

The Eye of the Storm
(JOB)
Author: Bryson Smith, 6 studies

The Search for Meaning
(ECCLESIASTES)
Author: Tim McMahon, 9 studies

Two Cities
(ISAIAH)
Authors: Andrew Reid and Karen Morris, 9 studies

Kingdom of Dreams
(DANIEL)
Authors: Andrew Reid and Karen Morris, 8 studies

Burning Desire
(OBADIAH & MALACHI)
Authors: Phillip Jensen and Richard Pulley, 6 studies

Warning Signs
(JONAH)
Author: Andrew Reid, 6 studies

Full of Promise
(THE BIG PICTURE OF THE O.T.)
Authors: Phil Campbell and Bryson Smith, 8 studies

The Good Living Guide
(MATTHEW 5:1-12)
Authors: Phillip Jensen and Tony Payne, 9 studies

News of the Hour
(MARK)
Author: Peter Bolt, 10 studies

Mission Unstoppable
(ACTS)
Author: Bryson Smith, 10 studies

The Free Gift of Life
(ROMANS 1-5)
Author: Gordon Cheng, 8 studies

Proclaiming the Risen Lord
(LUKE 24 – ACTS 2)
Author: Peter Bolt, 6 studies

Free for All
(GALATIANS)
Authors: Phillip Jensen and Kel Richards, 8 studies

Walk this Way
(EPHESIANS)
Author: Bryson Smith, 8 studies

Partners for Life
(PHILIPPIANS)
Author: Tim Thorburn, 8 studies

The Complete Christian
(COLOSSIANS)
Authors: Phillip Jensen and Tony Payne, 8 studies

To the Householder
(1 TIMOTHY)
Authors: Phillip Jensen and Greg Clarke, 9 studies

Run the Race
(2 TIMOTHY)
Author: Bryson Smith, 6 studies

The Path to Godliness
(TITUS)
Authors: Phillip Jensen and Tony Payne, 6 studies

From Shadow to Reality
(HEBREWS)
Author: Joshua Ng, 10 studies

The Implanted Word
(JAMES)
Authors: Phillip Jensen and Kirsten Birkett, 8 studies

Homeward Bound
(1 PETER)
Authors: Phillip Jensen and Tony Payne, 10 studies

All You Need to Know
(2 PETER)
Author: Bryson Smith, 6 studies

The Vision Statement
(REVELATION)
Author: Greg Clarke, 9 studies

Bold I Approach
(PRAYER)
Author: Tony Payne, 6 studies

Cash Values
(MONEY)
Author: Tony Payne, 5 studies

The Blueprint
(DOCTRINE)
Authors: Phillip Jensen and Tony Payne, 11 studies

Woman of God
(THE BIBLE ON WOMEN)
Author: Terry Blowes, 8 studies

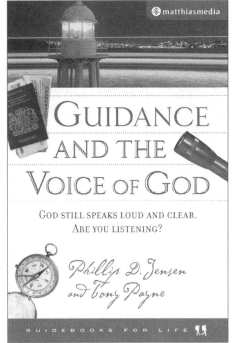

The How and Why of Love

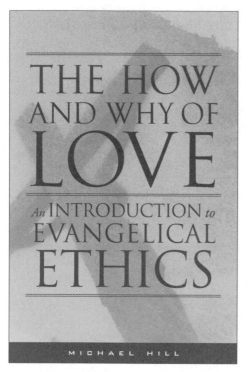

An Introduction to Evangelical Ethics

Is abortion ever right? Can divorced Christians remarry? What about euthanasia? In a whole range of issues, Christians search for the biblical answer. But ethics is about far more than controversial issues and hard cases. It's about how we apply the teaching of the Bible to our lives each day as we wait for Christ's return; it's about our actions and our motives; it's about our character. In this vibrant, stimulating and much-needed book, Michael Hill introduces us to an evangelical approach to ethics. Starting from creation, and taking us through the whole of biblical theology, the author develops a simple and yet comprehensive model of gospel-based ethics. In so doing, he provides us not just with solutions to difficult cases, but with an ethical framework we can bring to every aspect of our lives.

Tell us what you think about *Where to, Lord?*

Where to, Lord? is the first in Matthias Media's *Insight Studies* range. We'd like your comments and feedback so that we can continue to improve them as we go along. Please fill in the following questionnaire after you have completed the studies and return it to:

Matthias Media
PO Box 225
Kingsford NSW 2032

Or, email your suggestions to:
feedback@matthiasmedia.com.au

1. We don't want to know your name, but could you tell us your:
   sex_____ age_____

2. Are you a full-time Christian minister?
   ○ yes   ○ no

3. Did you do these studies:
   ○ by yourself
   ○ with one or two others
   ○ with a group of 5-10 others
   ○ with a group of more than 10

4. Did you find the studies:
   ○ too simplistic
   ○ about right
   ○ too intellectual

5. Did you feel that the studies were practical enough in their application?
   ○ yes   ○ no

6. How long, on average, did each study take to complete?

   _____

7. Did you find the *suggested timings for each study* in appendix 1:
   ○ did not allow enough time
   ○ were about right
   ○ allowed too much time
   ○ I did not refer to the suggested timings

8. Do you have any comments or suggestions about the suggested timing of each study?

9. Do you have any comments or suggestions about the content of each study?

10. Do you have any overall comments or suggestions?